THE
HISTORY OF THE FAMILY

A RECORD BOOK

ALAN HUTCHISON PUBLISHING CO. LTD.

EARLY HISTORY

IMPORTANT EVENTS

EARLY HISTORY

IMPORTANT EVENTS

The Last of England
Ford Madox Brown (1821-1893)

EARLY HISTORY

IMPORTANT EVENTS

Baron Cobham and his Family Attri. *Master of the Countess of Warwick*

EARLY HISTORY

IMPORTANT EVENTS

A Montgolfier Balloon at Aranjuez, c.1764 Antonia Carnicero (1748-1814)

PARENTS

GRANDPARENTS

OUR FAMILY TREE

WHO WE ARE
AND WHO WE
COME FROM

HUSBAND'S FULL NAME

WIFE'S FULL NAME

DATE OF MARRIAGE   PLACE OF MARRIAGE

OUR CHILDREN

HUSBAND'S FATHER

HUSBAND'S MOTHER

DATE OF MARRIAGE   PLACE OF MARRIAGE

CHILDREN

WIFE'S FATHER

WIFE'S MOTHER

DATE OF MARRIAGE   PLACE OF MARRIAGE

CHILDREN

HUSBAND'S PATERNAL GRANDFATHER

HUSBAND'S PATERNAL GRANDMOTHER

DATE OF MARRIAGE   PLACE OF MARRIAGE

CHILDREN

HUSBAND'S MATERNAL GRANDFATHER

HUSBAND'S MATERNAL GRANDMOTHER

DATE OF MARRIAGE   PLACE OF MARRIAGE

CHILDREN

WIFE'S PATERNAL GRANDFATHER

WIFE'S PATERNAL GRANDMOTHER

DATE OF MARRIAGE   PLACE OF MARRIAGE

CHILDREN

WIFE'S MATERNAL GRANDFATHER

WIFE'S MATERNAL GRANDMOTHER

DATE OF MARRIAGE   PLACE OF MARRIAGE

CHILDREN

GREAT GRANDPARENTS

HUSBAND'S GREAT GRANDFATHER

HUSBAND'S GREAT GRANDMOTHER

HUSBAND'S GREAT GRANDFATHER

HUSBAND'S GREAT GRANDMOTHER

HUSBAND'S GREAT GRANDFATHER

HUSBAND'S GREAT GRANDMOTHER

HUSBAND'S GREAT GRANDFATHER

HUSBAND'S GREAT GRANDMOTHER

WIFE'S GREAT GRANDFATHER

WIFE'S GREAT GRANDMOTHER

WIFE'S GREAT GRANDFATHER

WIFE'S GREAT GRANDMOTHER

WIFE'S GREAT GRANDFATHER

WIFE'S GREAT GRANDMOTHER

WIFE'S GREAT GRANDFATHER

WIFE'S GREAT GRANDMOTHER

GREAT, GREAT GRANDPARENTS

HUSBAND'S GREAT, GREAT GRANDFATHER

HUSBAND'S GREAT, GREAT GRANDMOTHER

HUSBAND'S GREAT, GREAT GRANDFATHER

HUSBAND'S GREAT, GREAT GRANDMOTHER

HUSBAND'S GREAT, GREAT GRANDFATHER

HUSBAND'S GREAT, GREAT GRANDMOTHER

HUSBAND'S GREAT, GREAT GRANDFATHER

HUSBAND'S GREAT, GREAT GRANDMOTHER

HUSBAND'S GREAT, GREAT GRANDFATHER

HUSBAND'S GREAT, GREAT GRANDMOTHER

HUSBAND'S GREAT, GREAT GRANDFATHER

HUSBAND'S GREAT, GREAT GRANDMOTHER

HUSBAND'S GREAT, GREAT GRANDFATHER

HUSBAND'S GREAT, GREAT GRANDMOTHER

HUSBAND'S GREAT, GREAT GRANDFATHER

HUSBAND'S GREAT, GREAT GRANDMOTHER

WIFE'S GREAT, GREAT GRANDFATHER

WIFE'S GREAT, GREAT GRANDMOTHER

WIFE'S GREAT, GREAT GRANDFATHER

WIFE'S GREAT, GRAT GRANDMOTHER

WIFE'S GREAT, GREAT GRANDFATHER

WIFE'S GREAT, GREAT GRANDMOTHER

WIFE'S GREAT, GREAT GRANDFATHER

WIFE'S GREAT, GREAT GRANDMOTHER

WIFE'S GREAT, GREAT GRANDFATHER

WIFE'S GREAT, GREAT GRANDMOTHER

WIFE'S GREAT, GREAT GRANDFATHER

WIFE'S GREAT, GREAT GRANDMOTHER

WIFE'S GREAT, GREAT GRANDFATHER

WIFE'S GREAT, GREAT GRANDMOTHER

WIFE'S GREAT, GREAT GRANDFATHER

WIFE'S GREAT, GREAT GRANDMOTHER

GREAT, GREAT, GREAT GRANDPARENTS

HUSBAND'S NAME

WIFE'S NAME

MR & MRS

MR & MRS

MR & MRS

MR & MRS

MR & MRS

MR & MRS

MR & MRS

MR & MRS

MR & MRS

MR & MRS

MR & MRS

MR & MRS

MR & MRS

MR & MRS

MR & MRS

MR & MRS

MR & MRS

MR & MRS

MR & MRS

MR & MRS

MR & MRS

MR & MRS

MR & MRS

MR & MRS

MR & MRS

MR & MRS

MR & MRS

MR & MRS

MR & MRS

MR & MRS

MR & MRS

MR & MRS

WIFE'S
GREAT GRANDPARENTS

MATERNAL

MR & MRS ....

DATE AND PLACE OF BIRTH ....

CHILDHOOD ....

....

MARRIAGE ....

....

BIRTH OF CHILDREN ....

....

HOMES ....

....

OCCUPATION ....

....

PERSONALITY AND DESCRIPTION ....

....

....

SPECIAL POINTS OF INTEREST ....

....

MR & MRS ....

DATE AND PLACE OF BIRTH ....

CHILDHOOD ....

....

MARRIAGE ....

....

BIRTH OF CHILDREN ....

....

HOMES ....

The Christening of the Princess Royal (detail)
C. R. Leslie (1749-1859)

OCCUPATION ....

....

PERSONALITY AND DESCRIPTION ....

....

....

SPECIAL POINTS OF INTEREST ....

....

GREAT GRANDPARENTS

PATERNAL

MR & MRS ....

DATE AND PLACE OF BIRTH ....

CHILDHOOD ....

....

MARRIAGE ....

....

BIRTH OF CHILDREN ....

....

HOMES ....

....

OCCUPATION ....

....

PERSONALITY AND DESCRIPTION ....

....

....

SPECIAL POINTS OF INTEREST ....

....

MR & MRS ....

DATE AND PLACE OF BIRTH ....

CHILDHOOD ....

....

MARRIAGE ....

....

BIRTH OF CHILDREN ....

....

HOMES ....

....

OCCUPATION ....

....

PERSONALITY AND DESCRIPTION ....

....

SPECIAL POINTS OF INTEREST ....

Fatherly Love (detail) Etienne Aubry (1745-1781)

GREAT GRANDPARENTS

MR & MRS ....

DATE AND PLACE OF BIRTH ....

CHILDHOOD ....

....

MARRIAGE ....

....

BIRTH OF CHILDREN ....

....

HOMES ....

....

OCCUPATION ....

....

PERSONALITY AND DESCRIPTION ....

....

....

SPECIAL POINTS OF INTEREST ....

....

MR & MRS ....

DATE AND PLACE OF BIRTH ....

CHILDHOOD ....

....

MARRIAGE ....

....

BIRTH OF CHILDREN ....

....

HOMES ....

....

OCCUPATION ....

....

PERSONALITY AND DESCRIPTION ....

....

....

SPECIAL POINTS OF INTEREST ....

....

MR & MRS ....

DATE AND PLACE OF BIRTH ....

CHILDHOOD ....

....

MARRIAGE ....

....

BIRTH OF CHILDREN ....

....

HOMES ....

....

OCCUPATION ....

....

PERSONALITY AND DESCRIPTION ....

....

....

SPECIAL POINTS OF INTEREST ....

....

PHOTOGRAPHS

MR & MRS

DATE AND PLACE OF BIRTH

CHILDHOOD

MARRIAGE

BIRTH OF CHILDREN

HOMES

OCCUPATION

PERSONALITY AND DESCRIPTION

SPECIAL POINTS OF INTEREST

Interior
Georg Nicolas Achen (1860-1912)

WIFE'S
GRANDPARENTS
MATERNAL

GRANDMOTHER ....

DATE AND PLACE OF BIRTH ....

CHILDHOOD ....

....

MARRIAGE ....

....

BIRTH OF CHILDREN ....

....

HOMES ....

....

OCCUPATION ....

....

PERSONALITY AND DESCRIPTION ....

....

....

SPECIAL POINTS OF INTEREST ....

....

Jardins du Luxembourg *Pierre de Belay (1890-1947)*

GRANDFATHER ....

DATE AND PLACE OF BIRTH ....

CHILDHOOD ....

....

MARRIAGE ....

....

BIRTH OF CHILDREN ....

....

HOMES ....

....

OCCUPATION ....

....

PERSONALITY AND DESCRIPTION ....

....

....

SPECIAL POINTS OF INTEREST ....

....

PHOTOGRAPHS

WIFE'S
GRANDPARENTS

PATERNAL

GRANDMOTHER ....

DATE AND PLACE OF BIRTH ....

CHILDHOOD ....

....

MARRIAGE ....

....

BIRTH OF CHILDREN ....

....

HOMES ....

....

OCCUPATION ....

....

PERSONALITY AND DESCRIPTION ....

....

....

SPECIAL POINTS OF INTEREST ....

....

WIFE'S
GRANDPARENTS

PATERNAL

GRANDFATHER ....

DATE AND PLACE OF BIRTH ....

CHILDHOOD ....

....

MARRIAGE ....

....

BIRTH OF CHILDREN ....

....

HOMES ....

....

OCCUPATION ....

....

PERSONALITY AND DESCRIPTION ....

....

....

SPECIAL POINTS OF INTEREST ....

....

Experiment with an Air Pump *Joseph Wright of Derby (1734-1797)*

GRANDMOTHER ....

DATE AND PLACE OF BIRTH ....

CHILDHOOD ....

....

MARRIAGE ....

....

BIRTH OF CHILDREN ....

....

HOMES ....

....

OCCUPATION ....

....

PERSONALITY AND DESCRIPTION ....

....

....

SPECIAL POINTS OF INTEREST ....

....

PHOTOGRAPHS

HUSBAND'S
GRANDPARENTS
MATERNAL

GRANDFATHER ....

DATE AND PLACE OF BIRTH ....

CHILDHOOD ....

....

MARRIAGE ....

....

BIRTH OF CHILDREN ....

....

HOMES ....

....

OCCUPATION ....

....

PERSONALITY AND DESCRIPTION ....

....

....

SPECIAL POINTS OF INTEREST ....

....

HUSBAND'S
GRANDPARENTS

PATERNAL

GRANDMOTHER ....

DATE AND PLACE OF BIRTH ....

CHILDHOOD ....

....

MARRIAGE ....

....

BIRTH OF CHILDREN ....

....

HOMES ....

....

OCCUPATION ....

....

PERSONALITY AND DESCRIPTION ....

....

....

SPECIAL POINTS OF INTEREST ....

....

HUSBAND'S
GRANDPARENTS

PATERNAL

GRANDFATHER ....

DATE AND PLACE OF BIRTH ....

CHILDHOOD ....

....

MARRIAGE ....

....

BIRTH OF CHILDREN ....

....

HOMES ....

....

OCCUPATION ....

....

PERSONALITY AND DESCRIPTION ....

....

....

SPECIAL POINTS OF INTEREST ....

....

PHOTOGRAPHS

WIFE'S
PARENTS

MOTHER ....

DATE AND PLACE OF BIRTH ....

CHILDHOOD ....

....

MARRIAGE ....

....

BIRTH OF CHILDREN ....

....

HOMES ....

....

OCCUPATION ....

....

PERSONALITY AND DESCRIPTION ....

....

....

SPECIAL POINTS OF INTEREST ....

....

WIFE'S
PARENTS

FATHER ....

DATE AND PLACE OF BIRTH ....

CHILDHOOD ....

....

MARRIAGE ....

....

BIRTH OF CHILDREN ....

....

HOMES ....

....

OCCUPATION ....

....

PERSONALITY AND DESCRIPTION ....

....

....

SPECIAL POINTS OF INTEREST ....

....

HUSBAND'S
PARENTS

MOTHER ....

DATE AND PLACE OF BIRTH ....

CHILDHOOD ....

....

MARRIAGE ....

....

BIRTH OF CHILDREN ....

....

HOMES ....

....

OCCUPATION ....

....

PERSONALITY AND DESCRIPTION ....

....

....

SPECIAL POINTS OF INTEREST ....

....

HUSBAND'S
PARENTS

FATHER ....

DATE AND PLACE OF BIRTH ....

CHILDHOOD ....

....

MARRIAGE ....

....

BIRTH OF CHILDREN ....

....

HOMES ....

....

OCCUPATION ....

....

PERSONALITY AND DESCRIPTION ....

....

....

SPECIAL POINTS OF INTEREST ....

....

The Wedding March Theodore Robinson (1852-1896)

Aunts Uncles Cousins

Wife

Aunts Uncles Cousins

Husband

Similar Physical Attributes

Eye Colour   Hair Colour   Heights   Distinguishing Marks

The Cholmondeley Sisters British School (17th century)

SIMILAR PHYSICAL ATTRIBUTES

EYE COLOUR   HAIR COLOUR   HEIGHTS   DISTINGUISHING MARKS

Similar Physical Attributes

Eye Colour   Hair Colour   Heights   Distinguishing Marks

SIMILAR PHYSICAL ATTRIBUTES

EYE COLOUR   HAIR COLOUR   HEIGHTS   DISTINGUISHING MARKS

SIMILAR PHYSICAL ATTRIBUTES

EYE COLOUR HAIR COLOUR HEIGHTS DISTINGUISHING MARKS

Alexander Cassatt and His Son Robert Kelso *Mary Cassatt (1844-1926)*

Talents

Music Dramatic

The Forgotten Melody Dame Ethel Walker (1867-1951)

TALENTS

MUSIC DRAMATIC

A Dress Rehearsal Frederick Barnard (1846-1896)

Talents

Artistic Creative

TALENTS

ARTISTIC CREATIVE

The Sketchers John Singer Sargent (1856-1925)

Talents

Athletic or Sporting

TALENTS

ATHLETIC OR SPORTING

Racing Cars Terence Cuneo (b.1907)

TALENTS

INTELLIGENCE PRACTICAL

TALENTS

INTELLIGENCE EDUCATION

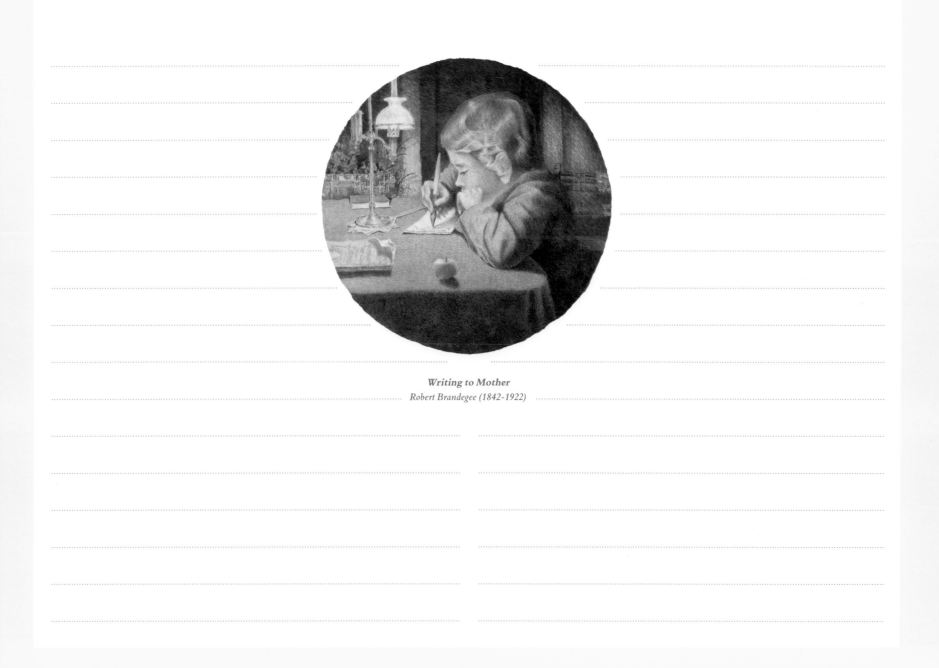

Writing to Mother
Robert Brandegee (1842-1922)

TALENTS

INTELLIGENCE EDUCATION

SIMILARITIES AND DIFFERENCES

INTELLIGENCE EDUCATION

Return to School 1833 (detail) *Henri Jules Jean Geoffroy (fl. 1883)*

SIMILARITIES AND DIFFERENCES

INTERESTS AND OCCUPATIONS

The Star *Edgar Degas (1834-1917)*

SIMILARITIES AND DIFFERENCES

INTERESTS AND OCCUPATIONS

Portrait of a Red Cross Nurse *Gabriel Emile Edouard Nicolet (1856-1921)*

Similarities and Differences

Likes and Dislikes

The Last Day in the Old Home Robert B. Martineau (1826-1869)

SIMILARITIES AND DIFFERENCES

SENSE OF HUMOUR

SIMILARITIES AND DIFFERENCES

RURAL OR URBAN

Similarities and Differences

Rural or Urban

Farmhouse and Chestnut Trees at Jas-de-Bouffan Paul Cézanne (1839-1906)

Wife

NAME .... DATE AND PLACE OF BIRTH ....

CHILDHOOD ....

....

MARRIAGE ....

....

BIRTH OF CHILDREN ....

....

HOMES ....

....

OCCUPATION ....

....

PERSONALITY AND DESCRIPTION ....

....

....

SPECIAL POINTS OF INTEREST ....

....

....

Husband

NAME .... DATE AND PLACE OF BIRTH ....

CHILDHOOD ....

....

MARRIAGE ....

....

BIRTH OF CHILDREN ....

....

HOMES ....

....

OCCUPATION ....

....

PERSONALITY AND DESCRIPTION ....

....

....

SPECIAL POINTS OF INTEREST ....

....

....

Children

Date and Place of Birth ....

Childhood ....

....

Marriage ....

....

Birth of Children ....

....

Homes ....

....

Occupation ....

....

Personality and Description ....

....

....

Special Points of Interest ....

....

....

Tea on the Grass Henri Lebasque (1865-1937)

CHILDREN

DATE AND PLACE OF BIRTH ....

CHILDHOOD ....

....

MARRIAGE ....

....

BIRTH OF CHILDREN ....

....

HOMES ....

....

OCCUPATION ....

....

PERSONALITY AND DESCRIPTION ....

....

....

SPECIAL POINTS OF INTEREST ....

....

....

Children

Date and Place of Birth ....

Childhood ....

....

Marriage ....

....

Birth of Children ....

....

Homes ....

....

Occupation ....

....

Personality and Description ....

....

....

Special Points of Interest ....

....

....

Children

Date and Place of Birth ....

Childhood ....

....

Marriage ....

....

Birth of Children ....

....

Homes ....

....

Occupation ....

....

Personality and Description ....

....

....

Special Points of Interest ....

....

....

CHILDREN

DATE AND PLACE OF BIRTH ....

CHILDHOOD ....

....

MARRIAGE ....

....

BIRTH OF CHILDREN ....

....

HOMES ....

....

OCCUPATION ....

....

PERSONALITY AND DESCRIPTION ....

....

....

SPECIAL POINTS OF INTEREST ....

....

....

PHOTOGRAPHS

CHILDREN

DATE AND PLACE OF BIRTH ....

CHILDHOOD ....

....

MARRIAGE ....

....

BIRTH OF CHILDREN ....

....

HOMES ....

....

OCCUPATION ....

....

PERSONALITY AND DESCRIPTION ....

....

....

SPECIAL POINTS OF INTEREST ....

....

....

CHILDREN

DATE AND PLACE OF BIRTH ....

CHILDHOOD ....

....

MARRIAGE ....

....

BIRTH OF CHILDREN ....

....

HOMES ....

....

OCCUPATION ....

....

PERSONALITY AND DESCRIPTION ....

....

....

SPECIAL POINTS OF INTEREST ....

....

....

PHOTOGRAPHS

Grandchildren

Date and Place of Birth ....

Childhood ....

....

Marriage ....

....

Birth of Children ....

....

Homes ....

....

Occupation ....

....

Personality and Description ....

....

....

Special Points of Interest ....

....

....

Boys and Kitten *Winslow Homer (1836-1910)*

Grandchildren

DATE AND PLACE OF BIRTH ....

CHILDHOOD ....

....

MARRIAGE ....

....

BIRTH OF CHILDREN ....

....

HOMES ....

....

OCCUPATION ....

....

PERSONALITY AND DESCRIPTION ....

....

....

SPECIAL POINTS OF INTEREST ....

....

....

GRANDCHILDREN

DATE AND PLACE OF BIRTH ....

CHILDHOOD ....

....

MARRIAGE ....

....

BIRTH OF CHILDREN ....

....

HOMES ....

....

OCCUPATION ....

....

PERSONALITY AND DESCRIPTION ....

....

....

SPECIAL POINTS OF INTEREST ....

....

....

GRANDCHILDREN

DATE AND PLACE OF BIRTH ....

CHILDHOOD ....

....

MARRIAGE ....

....

BIRTH OF CHILDREN ....

....

HOMES ....

....

OCCUPATION ....

....

PERSONALITY AND DESCRIPTION ....

....

....

SPECIAL POINTS OF INTEREST ....

....

....

PHOTOGRAPHS

Grandchildren

DATE AND PLACE OF BIRTH ....

CHILDHOOD ....

....

MARRIAGE ....

....

BIRTH OF CHILDREN ....

....

HOMES ....

....

OCCUPATION ....

....

PERSONALITY AND DESCRIPTION ....

....

....

SPECIAL POINTS OF INTEREST ....

....

....

....

GRANDCHILDREN

DATE AND PLACE OF BIRTH ....

CHILDHOOD ....

....

MARRIAGE ....

....

BIRTH OF CHILDREN ....

....

HOMES ....

....

OCCUPATION ....

....

PERSONALITY AND DESCRIPTION ....

....

....

SPECIAL POINTS OF INTEREST ....

....

....

Mrs Cassatt Reading to her Grandchildren, 1880 Mary Cassatt (1844-1926)

GRANDCHILDREN

DATE AND PLACE OF BIRTH ....

CHILDHOOD ....

....

MARRIAGE ....

....

BIRTH OF CHILDREN ....

....

HOMES ....

....

OCCUPATION ....

....

PERSONALITY AND DESCRIPTION ....

....

....

SPECIAL POINTS OF INTEREST ....

....

....

GRANDCHILDREN

DATE AND PLACE OF BIRTH ....

CHILDHOOD ....

....

MARRIAGE ....

....

BIRTH OF CHILDREN ....

....

HOMES ....

....

OCCUPATION ....

....

PERSONALITY AND DESCRIPTION ....

....

SPECIAL POINTS OF INTEREST ....

....

Family Portrait Albert Besnard (1849-1934)

Grandchildren

Date and Place of Birth ....

Childhood ....

....

Marriage ....

....

Birth of Children ....

....

Homes ....

....

Occupation ....

....

Personality and Description ....

....

....

Special Points of Interest ....

....

....

GRANDCHILDREN

DATE AND PLACE OF BIRTH ....

CHILDHOOD ....

....

MARRIAGE ....

....

BIRTH OF CHILDREN ....

....

HOMES ....

....

OCCUPATION ....

....

PERSONALITY AND DESCRIPTION ....

....

....

SPECIAL POINTS OF INTEREST ....

....

....

Grandchildren

Date and Place of Birth ....

Childhood ....

....

Marriage ....

....

Birth of Children ....

....

Homes ....

....

Occupation ....

....

Personality and Description ....

....

....

Special Points of Interest ....

....

....

The Open Air Breakfast *William Merritt Chase (1849-1916)*

FAMILY STORIES AND TRADITIONS

PAST AND PRESENT

FAMILY STORIES AND TRADITIONS

PAST AND PRESENT

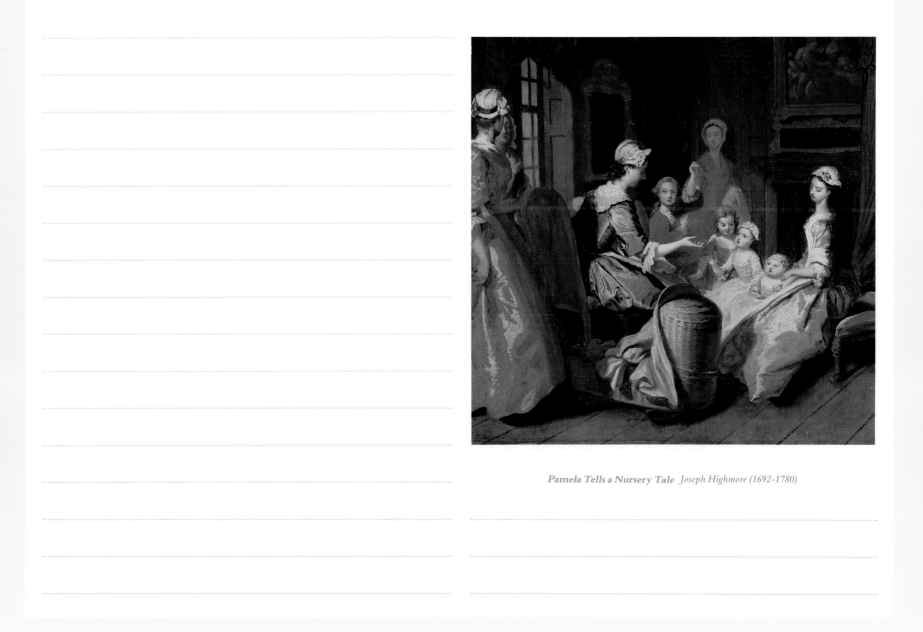

Pamela Tells a Nursery Tale Joseph Highmore (1692-1780)

FAMILY STORIES AND TRADITIONS

PAST AND PRESENT

FAMILY STORIES AND TRADITIONS

PAST AND PRESENT

The Warrior's Daughter *James Jacques Joseph Tissot (1836-1902)*

FAMILY STORIES AND TRADITIONS

PAST AND PRESENT

FAMILY HEIRLOOMS

The Banker's Private Room, Negotiating a Loan, 1870 John Callcot Horsley (1817-1903)

Family Heirlooms

FAMILY HEIRLOOMS

A Coming Event
Jessica Hayllar (1858-1940)
Forbes Magazine Collection, New York.

FAMILY HEIRLOOMS

FAMILY HEIRLOOMS

Still Life with Chinese Porcelain Bowl and Ewer Willem Kalf (1619-1693)

Unusual Incidents

Unusual Incidents

Firemen on the Roof *W. Matvyn Wright (b.1910)*

USEFUL SOURCES

General Register Office, *St Catherine's House, Kingsway, London WC2B 6JP*
Scottish Record Office, *PO Box 36, HM General Register House, Edinburgh EH1 3YY*
Public Record Office, *Land Registry Building, Portugal Street, London WC2A 1LR.*
COUNTY OR DIOCESAN RECORD OFFICES:
Society of Genealogists, *37 Harrington Gardens, London SW7 4JX*
Institute of Heraldic and Genealogical Studies, *Northgate, Canterbury, Society of
Antiquaries Burlington House, Piccadilly, London W1* **Society of Friends of St. George's
and the Descendants of the Knights of the Garter,** *Curfew Tower, Windsor Castle,
Windsor, Berks Heraldry Society, 28 Museum Street, London WC1A 1LH* **College of Arms,**
Queen Victoria Street, London Guildhall Library, Basinghall Street, London EC2 2EJ
Principal Probate Registry, *Somerset House, London WC2R 1LP* **National Register of Archives,**
Quality House, Quality Court, Chancery Lane, London WC2A 1HP.

COVER:
Street Scene in the Rain
Louis-Leopold Boilly (1761-1845)
Archiv für Kunst und Geschichte, Berlin

FRONTISPIECE:
The Jewish Bride
Rembrandt van Rijn (1606-1669)

The publishers are very grateful to the following organisations,
individuals and institutions for their kind permission to reproduce their pictures:
The Art Museum of the Atheneum, The Arthur and Margaret Glasgow Fund,
Virginia Museum of Fine Arts; Barber Institute of Fine Arts, The University of
Birmingham, Birmingham City Museums and Art Gallery; Bonham's, London;
The Bridgeman Art Library; The Brooklyn Museum; Christie's Colour Library; Private
Collection, The Clarendon Collection; The Fitzwilliam Museum, Cambridge; Laing Art
Gallery, Newcastle-upon-Tyne, Tyne and Wear Museums Service; The Marquess of Bath,
Longleat House; Reproduced by gracious permission of Her Majesty the Queen; Manchester
City Art Galleries; Musées Nationaux, France; The Norton Simon Foundation;
Photographie Giraudon; The Prado, Madrid; The Rijksmuseum, Amsterdam;
Royal Holloway and Bedford New College, Surrey; The Swedish National art Collection,
The Terra Museum of American Art, Chicago; Toledo Museum of Art;
Thyssen-Bornemisza Collection; Victoria and Albert Museum; Worcester
Art Museum, USA; W.P. Wilstach Collection, the Gift of
Mrs William Cox Wright, Philadelphia Museum of Art.

All the pictures in this book are either cropped or details from the original paintings

Published by Alan Hutchison Ltd
9 Pembridge Studios
27a Pembridge Villas
London W11 3EP

Worldwide distribution

Printed and bound in Hong Kong

Designed by Steve Kibble